IDEAS TO GO

SELF-ESTEEM

Ages 10-12

Activities and ideas to develop children's self-esteem,
across the Curriculum

Tanya Dalgleish

A & C Black • London

CONTENTS

INTRODUCTION

Good self-esteem has been shown to be vitally important for children's happiness, social and emotional well-being, and academic success. Mental health and well-being are key themes of the National Healthy Schools Programme, launched in 1999, which encourages schools to play a part in improving children's health. This book provides teachers with ideas and activities to help pupils develop their self-esteem. The activities make an ideal complement to classroom work across the Curriculum. They can be used in isolation, in sequence, or dipped into, as teachers require. The activities will help children to value themselves as individuals and to value the individuality of others, while appreciating concepts such as co-operation, negotiation and tolerance.

ABOUT THIS BOOK

TEACHERS' FILE

The teachers' file offers advice on how to make the most of this book. It offers ideas for classroom organisation as well as ICT tips, assessment ideas and suggestions for parental involvement.

QUICK STARTS

This section offers activity and game ideas that help to promote children's self-esteem. The activities require little or no preparation and can be used across various learning areas to complement existing lesson plans.

ACTIVITY BANK

The activity bank contains 28 photocopiable activities which cover five topic areas: valuing self; valuing others; feelings and emotions; strengths and limitations; and likes and dislikes. The activities can be used in any order and can be adapted to suit individual pupils or classes.

Photocopiable activities

CHALLENGES

These photocopiable task cards offer creative investigational challenges. They can be given to individual pupils or groups, and they can be used at any time and in any order. The task cards involve pupils in in following instructions and completing tasks independently.

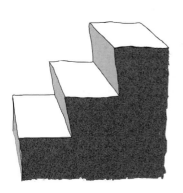

HOW TO USE THIS BOOK

QUICK STARTS

Quick starts are ideal warm-up activities for the beginning of a lesson. Each activity is intended to provide 10–15 minutes of group or whole class discussion. Reflect on the completed task with the children. Ask what they learnt and whether there was anything that surprised them.

Example Advertising (page 14) is an opportunity for small group work. Each group could research a different medium so that comparisons can be made. Children could then adapt advertisements for different media, providing a variety of outcomes for display.

Advertising

Pupils, in small groups, design a television advertisement (see page 42) promoting an admirable personality trait: loyalty, honesty, reliability or optimism are examples. Pupils should consider target audiences, e.g. middle/upper primary pupils, teenagers, young adults. Allow time for planning, creating and presentation. Pupils then assess the other advertisements, discussing stereotyping, gender representation, ethnicity, age, socio-economic status or disability. Advertisements could be adapted for other media (radio, magazines, leaflets, stickers, badges).

Likes and Dislikes   NAME Joe Harris   6?

At School

Things I enjoy about school.
I enjoy school because I like learning and doing things for the teachers.

Things I dislike about school.
I dislike people making fun of me and other people, and bullying.

Things I do well.
I do well in science and math because I have got more confident on my maths.

Areas that need improvement.
My english I need to improve because I need to get my puctuation and spelling a bit better.

Activities I'd like to do more of.
I like to do more sport and more.

ACTIVITY BANK

These photocopiable activities can be used by individuals, groups or the whole class. They could provide the focus for a whole lesson. The activities will not in themselves achieve the objectives, but they will make children start to think about these very complex issues. Many of the activities touch on sensitive issues, particularly for pupils with low self-esteem; take this into consideration when introducing the activities and discussing outcomes. It is helpful to make it clear to pupils whether the activity is to be private or shared, especially for pupils at the top end of Key Stage 2.

Example At school (page 40) helps to teach children to value themselves as individuals, and then value the individuality of others. This sheet could be private, or shared with an adult or another child.

CHALLENGES

These photocopiable activities are perfect for use in learning centres, in the school library or in the classroom. The investigational nature of the activities is in line with National Curriculum requirements and supports the development of investigational problem-solving skills.

Example Coping with disabilities (page 45) could be followed up with feedback from the local community. Children could ask disabled pupils or adults about their day at school or at home and find out their responses to issues raised by the activity.

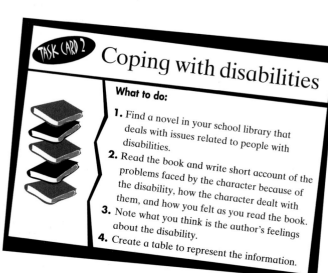

TASK CARD 2   Coping with disabilities

What to do:

1. Find a novel in your school library that deals with issues related to people with disabilities.
2. Read the book and write short account of the problems faced by the character because of the disability, how the character dealt with them, and how you felt as you read the book.
3. Note what you think is the author's feelings about the disability.
4. Create a table to represent the information.

TEACHERS' FILE

ABOUT SELF-ESTEEM

Motivation

The most important form of motivation is intrinsic motivation, which comes from within the child instead of being aimed at external reward or praise. Children who feel good about themselves are intrinsically motivated. They are more likely to be successful. For example, pupils who feel good about their reading ability choose to read and therefore become better readers. Success in one area allows pupils to be risk-takers and triers in other areas. The key for the teacher is to find an area in which the pupil excels and use that success as a springboard for other successes. Teachers can use a survey to find out about children's interests and other things they may be good at.

What is Self-esteem?

Self-esteem means how we feel about ourselves. For a child, self-esteem can involve: how you think you are regarded by your family, teachers and classmates; how you feel about yourself as a pupil or as a friend; whether you think other pupils like you or not; and how effective you feel you are in managing your life. Children who feel 'different' tend to have lower self-esteem. If children have negative feelings about themselves, they are more likely to display negative feelings towards others, to underachieve in school, and to develop behavioural problems and/or anti-social behaviour.

Early childhood is the optimum time to foster self-esteem in children; the older a child becomes, the harder it is to counter the effects of low self-esteem. It is important to help pupils maintain a balanced view of themselves, which includes recognising and valuing their own strengths while accepting their limitations. Encourage pupils to set realistic goals. Simply 'to be the best you can be' is a worthwhile goal. If teachers encourage pupils to value themselves as individuals and to value the individuality of others, while reinforcing the importance of co-operation and tolerance, pupils will develop a positive, optimistic outlook on life.

Friendship

It is vital for children's self-esteem for them to feel that they are accepted by their teachers and classmates. Help children to understand that they don't have to like or be liked by everyone, but they do need to accept and be accepted by others. You could model how to give and receive compliments, and demonstrate how you value and respect each child and his or her feelings.

Conflict resolution

Explain to pupils how they can try to resolve conflict. You could introduce children to the following process:
● Articulate the problem
● Discuss possible solutions
● Make a choice about a solution
● Reflect on the outcome

CLASSROOM ORGANISATION

How to use this book (page 4) suggests a range of approaches for using self-esteem activities in the classroom. The activities in this book could also be used in the following ways:

- For individuals during a wet playtime
- In small groups with a Learning Support Assistant
- As homework for a PSE lesson on a related theme
- As a focus for a circle time discussion for a small group
- For paired reading in Literacy
- For individuals working with parents or an older pupil

In promoting mutual respect, co-operation and individuality, it is also useful to consider the parts played by the classroom environment, accessibility of resources and classroom management.

The classroom environment

A supportive classroom environment makes pupils feel secure and helps them to face the challenges presented by school life. Children know that they will be listened to, their contributions will be valued and their opinions respected. It takes time to establish this kind of environment, but the benefits for teachers as well as pupils are worth the effort. The teacher should aim to put aside any personal feelings towards particular pupils and take positive steps to respect and value all pupils equally.

When something positive is achieved by the class, make the most of it by focusing pupils' attention on the achievement. Pupils could write the outcome on a chart for display, for example, 'We worked together to perform the class play' or 'We helped each other learn our spelling words'. Display pupils' work and allow opportunities for them to respond to each other's work, for example, 'I like that painting because I like the bright colours.' Help pupils to develop appropriate language and vocabulary for commenting on each other's work. If possible, ensure that something positive is said about each pupil's efforts.

At the end of every day, try to allow time for reflection. Reflection gives children time to think about what they have done, attempted or achieved. When given opportunities to reflect, pupils learn to recognise and take pleasure in what they have accomplished.

Ways to enhance the learning environment:
- Improve the classroom layout and use displays as visual stimuli
- Select teaching methods and organisational strategies appropriate to the pupils' needs
- Create a learning environment of high challenge and low stress
- Establish a positive, welcoming atmosphere
- Vary the way pupils work – for example, independently or in small groups
- Aim for a balance between structured and unstructured tasks
- Use a variety of learning styles – for example, hands on, visual, oral, written
- Establish the 'big picture' by linking tasks with pupils' experiences
- Use music to enhance the learning environment and to improve the children's ability to recall information

Cooperative learning

Co-operative learning activities encourage communication, collaboration and negotiation. They can lead to a deeper understanding of subject matter, higher self-esteem and greater self-confidence. Through sharing their skills, pupils learn that they are accepted by others and valued as group members. Co-operation can be encouraged through games and group activities such as multi-voice recitation and science experiments. Aim to provide a balance of co-operative and independent activities. Some gifted pupils may become frustrated if they are always asked to work collaboratively; they need also to work on independent tasks that they can pursue at length and to the best of their abilities.

Bibliotherapy

Books can be used in the classroom to help pupils understand their own problems. Children often find it easy to identify and empathise with characters in literature, by relating the characters' situations to their own. Using literature in this way helps children to realise that there are other children in similar positions to themselves. They also learn that problems can be faced and usually solved. If you are aware of a pupil with a particular difficulty (for example, divorce in the family, death of a pet, disability, shyness or bullying), you could choose a relevant story for the children to read, showing sensitivity about why that particular book is being read.

Games

Games in which everyone co-operates and all pupils are winners can play a part in establishing a classroom environment that promotes pupils' self-esteem. Competition has a place, but in games where there are winners and losers, the loser may feel miserable. It is important to ensure that no pupil continually loses or is always picked last when forming teams.

Self-esteem learning centres

A self-esteem learning centre could be set up in part of the classroom or as a shared resource for the whole school, perhaps in part of the school library. The learning centre might contain relevant books, jigsaw puzzles, maths equipment, construction blocks, a listening post, paper, pencils and a supply of art materials. It is a good idea to set up folders of blank worksheets and add new ones regularly. Provide a set of activity cards, some of which could be topic-based and some generic, for example, 'Research a favourite animal', 'Write a poem about your favourite food', 'Work in a group to conduct the following experiment', and so on. Provide activities that allow for both independent and group work. A computer is useful for encouraging pupils to use software collaboratively. You could also provide a book in which pupils can record discoveries or useful tips for pupils working there in future.

Grouping children

Grouping pupils in different ways allows for a variety of interactions amongst them. Groups may be homogeneous (pupils of similar abilities, interests or backgrounds) or heterogeneous (pupils of differing abilities, interests or backgrounds). Smaller groups generally work best because they allow all pupils to participate in the discussion. The teacher can assign roles within the group or ask the group to decide who should do which jobs. Ensure that over time, every pupil has an opportunity to take on each of the roles. Roles may vary according to the tasks involved and particular pupils' needs, but you could use this list as a starting point.

- **Recorder** - makes notes of important points or decisions
- **Reporter** - reports to class on discussions
- **Questioner** - prompts discussion by questioning and clarifying issues
- **Observer** - acts as a witness and later reports how the group achieved it's goals
- **Motivator** - encourages all group members

ICT TIPS

ICT skills can be integrated into many aspects of learning. If computers are to become a valuable part of the classroom, it must be easy for children to use them independently. It can be a help to have a parent rota which arranges for a parent to sit at the computer with children and offer assistance when needed.

Choose software that provides opportunities for positive interaction between the children in a group, and between children and adults. Software can encourage problem-solving and the use of thinking skills, while including fun aspects such as music and animation. This will improve children's self-esteem by allowing them to solve problems, make decisions and work co-operatively with others. Avoid programs that require reading skills beyond the children's ability, or are too difficult for children to navigate, as these will lead to feelings of frustration and incompetence.

It is important to let pupils make mistakes along with their successes. Pupils will learn by trying things out on their own, and by talking about what worked and what did not. Be willing to listen to and discuss what students have done and what they have discovered.

Communication via e-mail can help to boost the confidence of students who are unsure of their communication skills, because there is no need for visual and non-verbal conversational cues. E-mail offers pupils the opportunity to correspond with a wide range of people as they develop their ICT skills. E-mail can be used in the classroom for various educational purposes. Activities could incorporate the following ideas:

- Allow children to e-mail organisations such as charities to ask for information related to projects they are studying
- Set up links with other classes and pupils so that children can collaborate on projects and lessons
- Arrange for pupils to become e-pals with other pupils around the world

ASSESSMENT

Self-esteem can be assessed by observing students over time. The following questions may be useful for assessment.

- Are pupils willing to take risks in their work and play, for example by using approximate spellings?
- Are they confident enough to 'have a go'?
- Are they eager to try new experiences and challenges?
- Are they positive in their reactions to new experiences?
- Do they make friends easily?
- Can they set goals for themselves?

- Are they positive in their reactions to teacher expectations?
- Are they realistic in their expectations of themselves?
- Can they accept defeat?
- Are they willing to learn from their mistakes?
- How do they cope with problems and set-backs?
- Are they confident enough to contribute to class discussions?

Encourage pupils to assess their own work, which could involve keeping folders of their best or most enjoyable projects. The aim is for children to be intrinsically motivated to do their best. Learning to evaluate their own efforts allows them to rely on their own values rather than on outside judgements.

PARENTAL INVOLVEMENT

It is beneficial to explain to parents why self-esteem is important for children's academic success, their happiness, and their social and emotional well-being. Explain that children who have negative feelings about themselves are more likely to display negative feelings towards others and to underachieve in school. You could inform parents that you want the children to achieve the following goals:

- To value themselves as individuals
- To value the individuality of others
- To work with others co-operatively
- To learn negotiation skills
- To appreciate the value of tolerance
- To learn how to make effective decisions for themselves

Invite parents to participate in classroom activities by sharing their skills or knowledge with pupils. Encourage them to share aspects of their cultural backgrounds through activities such as cooking, language, art, music and dance. You could involve the class and parents in community-based events such as Senior Citizens Week.

Ask parents to support your efforts at home by allowing children to make everyday choices such as what the family will have for dinner. In this way parents can let children know that their opinions are valued and respected. Suggest that parents phrase ground rules positively rather than negatively, saying, for example, 'When your room is tidy you can watch television,' rather than, 'If you don't tidy your room you won't be allowed to watch television.'

QUICK STARTS

Polarised debate

Choose a topic. Arrange pupils in a semicircle — those agreeing with the topic on the right, those disagreeing on the left, and those undecided across the top. Pupils from each group, in turn, present their opinions, without interruption. Pupils can change positions during the debate. Suggest pupils be tolerant of other opinions. If either side lacks numbers, you can play 'devil's advocate'.

Just the facts

Read a factual text to pupils, asking them to note key words and phrases. Reread, allowing pupils to correct their notes. Have them, in small groups, combine notes to develop an information report; they should consider structure of the text and information accuracy. The children then read other groups' work and compare. Reread the original text, asking how they believe their notes reflect this information. Encourage open, positive self- and peer assessment.

Let's discuss it

Suggest students write a discussion text based on arguments presented in the polarised debate. A discussion needs to present all sides of an issue, using phrases such as 'some people believe that', 'other people believe that'. Model how to write a discussion text, or construct the discussion text with students. Explain that people are entitled to differing opinions and that differing opinions should be respected.

Writing playscripts

Each child chooses a picture book or novel section demonstrating a character's admirable trait, then constructs a playscript. Discuss movement, dialogue, narration, costume, make-up, lighting, sets and music. Explain that plays are stories (narrative) requiring orientation, complication, a series of events and a resolution. The audience needs to experience empathy for the characters. Allow time for rehearsal before performing some of the plays. Discuss the admirable qualities demonstrated.

Role models

Suggest pupils research modern-day heroes: these could include high-profile women, disabled athletes or heroes from other ethnic backgrounds. On completion of the research pupils can:
- role-play interviews with the hero
- write newspaper articles about events in the hero's life
- create a timeline showing events in the hero's life
- write a script for a ceremony honouring the hero
- design a postage stamp honouring the hero.

This is Your Life!

Group children in pairs to research a famous role model of their choice. They are to use their research findings to present a 'This is Your Life' about the person to the class. Suggest that pupils create documents such as birth certificates, passports and correspondence from friends. They can write newspaper articles about the person, and role play the various characters in the person's life.

In the hot seat

The pupil in the hot seat chooses a book character, a famous person or someone they know. The pupil is interviewed by classmates or chairs a panel discussion about relevant topics. When pupils role play characters in novels, classmates can interview them about events in their lives before or after those described in the novel. Pupils can then create a prologue or epilogue for the novel.

Read all about it!

Create a class newspaper, written by pupils, that includes positive articles about fellow pupils. Ensure that all class members are noted for their outstanding achievements in some aspect of school life, or include interviews with class members about their home background and achievements. Ensure there is a balance of academic, sporting, artistic, personal and social achievements.

Character portraits

Have pupils construct profiles for characters they admire in novels, films or television shows. Ensure that they describe the character's personality and state why they admire them. Discuss these characters, listing their admirable traits. Discuss where and when pupils could exhibit any of these traits. Discuss unlikely heroes, e.g., Flick in 'A Bug's Life', an accident-prone inventor not considered courageous, who triumphs in a plot where brain outsmarts brawn.

Exploring characterisation

• Ask the children to write diaries for characters in a novel.
• Have the children choose sections that indicate how characters feel and read these sections to each other in groups, discussing how characters feel about events, and how readers are enabled to empathise with them.
• The children can also create profiles, passports, school reports, letters or journals for their characters

Freeze frames

Group pupils to prepare freeze frames representing emotions (e.g., fear, jealousy, anger, sadness) experienced by a character in a class novel. They should consider gesture, body language and facial expression. After rehearsal, frames are shown, in sequence and in silence, to an audience. The audience closes their eyes while frames are set up, then opens them for 10 seconds to view the frame, and so on. Discuss aspects of the frames.

Pen-pals

Set up a classroom letterbox system and encourage pupils to exchange letters. Organise pen pals in a school in a different geographic area (i.e. city/country, small/large town, inner city/suburbs). Suggest they introduce themselves, write about whatever they are most interested in, and ask questions to find out about the person they are writing to. Suggest they include photos. Create a table showing how the schools and the students' lifestyles differ.

Reading conferences

Organise pupil reading conferences to discuss books they have read. Suggest that pupils structure the discussions around the following concepts: themes, settings, characters, problems faced by the characters, how the characters overcame their problems, the lessons learned by the characters and the moral of the story, if it has one.

Advertising

Pupils, in small groups, design a television advertisement (see page 42) promoting an admirable personality trait: loyalty, honesty, reliability or optimism are examples. Pupils should consider target audiences, e.g., middle/upper primary pupils, teenagers, young adults. Allow time for planning, creating and presentation. Pupils then assess the other advertisements, discussing stereotyping, gender representation, ethnicity, age, socio-economic status or disability. Advertisements could be adapted for other media (radio, magazines, leaflets, stickers, badges).

Talk-back radio

Create a radio talk-back show where themes and issues from a novel are discussed. Some pupils can be the panelists, who are characters from the novel, or 'experts' (e.g. psychiatrists, police, teachers, lawyers). Panelists introduce themselves to the live audience. One child is the host, ensuring each panelist is heard. Members of the audience 'phone in' and ask questions or express opinions. Tape-record the discussion for the class to hear.

A novel approach

Choose a class novel. Have pupils:

- Think about which character(s) they would like as a friend? Why? Ask them to write about it
- Imagine they are newspaper reporters witnessing the events. Write an article about one of the events, including interview quotes. Write a sensational headline, including illustrations

Even more novel...

Using a class novel, have students:

- Create a comic strip or cartoon based on the novel
- Scriptwrite part of the story. Rehearse with some friends and perform for the class.
- Write a poem expressing thoughts and feelings as they read the story ending

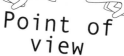

Point of view

Have pupils write about a class experience, using their own point of view, including feelings about the events. Compile individual entries into a class book, allowing pupils time to read all recounts. Note how they see things differently. Literature can show the significance of points of view. Have pupils write diary entries for characters involved in conflict. Explain how differing points of view can colour fact representation.

The news in pictures

Group pupils, distributing one newspaper photograph to each group. Have the children examine these photographs considering: their reactions, what is or is not represented, the camera angles used, the cropping of the photo, what point of view and emotions are represented? Each group creates a dramatisation, ending with the photo being taken. Pupils write an accompanying article, including a sensational headline, lead and story written in newsworthy rather than chronological order.

Journal keeping

Suggest that pupils keep journals. The journals can be purely personal documents like diaries, or they can be used for two-way correspondence between teacher and pupil. Pupils could use their journals to record their thoughts and opinions during a polarised debate. Journals can also be used for commenting on class novels and other classroom-based learning experiences.

ACTIVITY
BANK

Self-profile

Respond to each question honestly.

Are you eager to try new experiences and challenges?_____

Are you positive in your reactions to new experiences or the

thought of new experiences?_____

Are you positive in your reactions to teacher expectations? _____

Can you set goals for yourself?_____

Are you realistic in your expectations of yourself?_____

Can you accept defeat?_____

Can you learn from your mistakes?_____

How do you cope with problems and setbacks?_____

_____

Do you feel comfortable contributing to class discussions?_____

Do you make friends easily?_____

Self-assesses confidence and capabilities.

NAME

Acrostic poem

Write an acrostic poem to describe yourself.

e.g.   **J**umps high on the basketball court
       Always there when food's around
       Sings a bit off-key
       Outdoors type
       Never late for training

Helps identify individual characteristics.

That's like me

Choose a character from a novel you have read who is *most* like you. Write a description of the character and then explain how the character is like you.

_____

_____

_____

_____

_____

_____

_____

I'm not like that!

Choose a character in a novel you have read who is *least* like you. Write a description of the character and then explain how the character is not like you.

_____

_____

_____

_____

_____

_____

_____

Encourages comparisons and contrasts individual characteristics with those of others.

NAME

Once upon a time

Write a recount about something that has been a significant event in your life.

_____

_____

_____

_____

_____

_____

_____

_____

_____

_____

_____

Encourages thought of significant events in own life.

NAME

I dream . . .

What do you daydream about? Write about it here.

_____

_____

_____

_____

_____

_____

_____

_____

_____

_____

_____

_____

Helps expression of dreams and desires.

NAME

An autobiography for the future

Imagine that it is now the year 2040. Write an autobiography describing your life since leaving primary school.

_____

_____

_____

_____

_____

_____

_____

_____

_____

_____

_____

_____

_____

_____

_____

_____

_____

_____

_____

_____

Imaginatively looks to the future.

NAME

School report

Write a school report card for yourself.

English	
Maths	
PSHE	
PE/sport	
Arts/Music	
History/Geography	
RE	
Science	
ICT/DT	

Assesses own abilities.

NAME

My life

Create a timeline for your life so far, then create a design to represent your life on the nine panels of the 'quilt' below. On the quilt you might include significant people, events, things and places.

Identifies people, events, things and places of personal significance.

NAME

The drama unfolds...

Write a story based on the pupils in your own class.
Use the table below to plan your story.

Orientation	
Characters	
Setting	
Complication	
What problems do the characters face?	
Sequence of events outline	
Resolution	
What happens in the end?	
How is the complication resolved?	

Considers ways of working with peers.

NAME

Someone important

Write a poem about someone who is important to you. Describe what the person means to you and why.

Describes the significance to them of a particular person.

NAME

Friendly qualities

The following are traits you might value in a friend. Number them from 1 to 7, with 1 being the most important to you, and 7 being the least important.

honesty_____   generosity _____

courage _____   kindness _____

thoughtfulness _____   sense of humour _____

loyalty _____

Why is the trait you labelled 1 the most important to you? _____

_____

_____

Discuss your responses with a partner.

Considers and assesses the importance of various qualities in a friend.

NAME

When I met my friend . . .

Can you remember the first time you met one of your friends? Write about it on the lines below.

_____

_____

_____

_____

_____

_____

_____

_____

_____

_____

_____

_____

_____

_____

Considers events and feelings in the forming of a relationship.

NAME

A difference of opinion

Do you think it is better to be a girl or a boy? Consider things like school, home, social life and your future. Think about whether people treat girls and boys differently. Write which you think is better. Give reasons and include any difficulties you can think of in being a girl or a boy.

_____

_____

_____

_____

_____

_____

_____

_____

_____

Considers the implications of sexism, and states their own position.

Role play cards

Work with a partner. Cut out the cards below.
Choose a card and act out the scenario for your class.

A friend asks to borrow your favourite possession. You want to say no but you need to be tactful.

A person from your class whom you don't like very much has asked you to a party. What do you say and do?

A friend borrowed something from you and has not returned it. How do you get it back?

You borrowed something from a friend and accidentally broke it. What do you say to your friend?

Your friend has won a trophy but cheated to get it. What do you do?

You have won first prize for something that your friend can do really well too. Your friend did not win anything. What do you say to your friend?

Considers problems of ethics, emotion and responsibility

Book characters

Choose a novel in which there is a character you admire or believe in. Write your opinions of the character on the lines below.

Book title:

Opinion statement

_____

_____

_____

Arguments to support your opinion

_____

_____

_____

_____

_____

_____

_____

_____

_____

Summing up (restatement of opinion)

_____

_____

_____

_____

Gives arguments to support an opinion.

Improvisation

Work in pairs. Cut out the cards and place them face down.
Select one and create an improvisation that communicates the
word on the card. You could perform it for the class, and see if
they can guess which quality you are demonstrating.

friendship	tolerance
co-operation	negotiation
co-existence	truthfulness
trust	honesty
courage	acceptance

Creates an improvisation to demonstrate an abstract quality.

NAME

Handy advice

Write advice to help a new child in your class settle in with the teacher and your school rules.

_____

_____

_____

_____

_____

_____

_____

_____

_____

_____

_____

_____

_____

_____

_____

_____

_____

_____

_____

_____

_____

_____

_____

_____

Considers and communicates codes of behaviour.

How I feel

Complete the following sentences:

1. I feel annoyed when _____

_____

_____

2. I feel jealous when _____

_____

3. I feel upset when _____

_____

_____

4. I am happiest when _____

_____

_____

5. I am angry when _____

_____

_____

6. I am disappointed in myself when _____

_____

_____

7. I am proud of myself when _____

_____

_____

Identifies individual characteristics and feelings.

NAME

I can be good at...

Everyone has things they are good at and things they have to work hard at and practise.

List five things you are good at.

_____

_____

_____

_____

_____

List five things you would like to be good at.

_____

_____

_____

_____

_____

List five things you can practise and become good at.

_____

_____

_____

_____

_____

Assesses own skills and abilities and areas which could be improved.

NAME

We all have strengths

Everyone has things they are particularly good at.
Write the name of a classmate on each line.

Who can help you . . .

 read and understand a challenging novel? _____

 do your maths homework? _____

 prepare for a debate? _____

Who would you choose . . .

 to go with you to the school nurse if you were injured?

_____

 to help you find something you'd lost? _____

 to help you explain something to the head teacher?

_____

Who would sympathise if your feelings were hurt?

_____

Who helps cheer you up if you're feeling down?

_____

Assesses others' strengths and abilities.

NAME

Favourite things poems

What things do you like? Talk about them with a friend. Write down a list of all the things you can think of that you like. Now write a poem here using the list as a starting point. (You don't have to include everything on the list.)

Identifies and expresses own likes.

NAME

My favourite place

Think about a place you like to go to. It could be your bedroom, somewhere outdoors, your grandparent's house, or anywhere else you like to be. Write a description of this place for someone who has never seen it. Include the reasons why you like this place.

_____

_____

_____

_____

_____

_____

_____

_____

_____

_____

_____

_____

On art paper, create a painting or drawing that expresses your feelings about this place.

Identifies and expresses own likes, in writing and art.

NAME

My TV family

If you could become part of a family on television, which family would you choose to belong to and why? Would you be yourself or would you change in some way to fit into the family? Explain your choice and reasons.

_____

_____

_____

_____

_____

_____

_____

_____

_____

_____

_____

_____

_____

_____

_____

_____

_____

Identifies own likes; imagines self in a new situation.

Likes and dislikes

NAME

At school

Things I enjoy about school

_____

_____

_____

Things I dislike about school

_____

_____

_____

Things I do well

_____

_____

_____

Areas that need improvement

_____

_____

_____

Activities I'd like to do more of

_____

_____

_____

Identifies own likes, dislikes and abilities.

NAME

It happens every day

Poems often make us look at everyday things in a new or different way. Find a poem about an everyday experience (eating, sleeping, bathing, brushing your teeth). Talk to a partner about it.

Think of another everyday experience or thing. Write a poem about it that describes your exact experience.

Considers and communicates own experience creatively.

NAME

Television advertisement

Design a television advertisement for an admirable quality.

Admirable quality to be advertised:	
Target audience:	
Characters (everyday people, animated, experts, famous people?)	
Setting	
Speech (conversation, voice-over, dialogue, to camera?)	
Music/jingle	
Slogan	

Considers and communicates positive features of abstract qualities.

Pupil awards

Name _____

has shown empathy
for others.

Signed _____
Date _____

Name _____

has shown an
ability to negotiate.

Signed _____
Date _____

Name _____

is willing to 'have a go'
at tasks such as

_____

Signed _____
Date _____

Name _____

can solve problems
for her/himself.

Signed _____
Date _____

Name _____

can set goals for
him/herself.

Signed _____
Date _____

Name _____

is able to accept setbacks
and work with them.

Signed _____
Date _____

CHALLENGES

Bullying

What to do:

1. Work with a group and create a dramatisation that demonstrates bullying.

2. Perform it for an audience, then choose members of the audience to role-play witnesses giving evidence in court. One of the group members can act as judge.

3. Write a newspaper article about the events. Include quotes from the main characters and from witnesses to the events. Write a sensational headline and draw the photo that would accompany the article.

Coping with disabilities

What to do:

1. Find a novel in your school library that deals with issues related to people with disabilities.

2. Read the book and write short account of the problems faced by the character with the disability, how the character dealt with them and how you felt as you read the book.

3. Note what you think is the author's feelings about the disability.

4. Create a table to represent the information.

Sell yourself!

What to do:

1. Create an advertisement about yourself to sell yourself to a prospective employer. You could create a television, radio or magazine advertisement.

2. Carefully consider the different features of advertisements in each medium. What job are you applying for? What things are you going to say about yourself to show that you are suitable for the job? How are you going to get your message across?

Take my advice

What to do:

1. Find examples of advice columns in newspapers.

2. Examine the wording of these columns and then work with a partner to write an advice column of your own. This could deal with personal problems, or an area of expertise such as using computers, playing computer games, caring for pets, good books, cooking, sport or television.

3. Write three letters from imaginary correspondents detailing their problems, then answer them.

4. Publish your advice column for your classmates to read.

Laughter is good

TASK CARD 5

What to do:

1. Work with a group and consult with the school's librarian to choose examples in literature that show different types of humour, e.g., play-on-words, slapstick, or parody. You could use picture books or novels.

2. Create a chart that lists each book's title, classifies the type of humour and gives an example of the humour.

3. Talk to a partner about the meaning of the phrase 'Laughter is the best medicine'.

4. Report your findings to your class.

Where in the world?

TASK CARD 6

What you need:

- atlas or globe
- travel guides or books by travellers

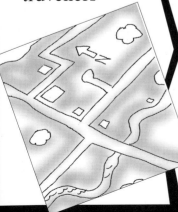

What to do:

1. If you could travel anywhere in the world, where would you go?

2. Research your chosen destination and means of getting there.

3. Write a letter or postcard to your class as if you are really there, telling them about your experiences.

4. Compile a table that lists the similarities and differences between the destination and where you live, and describe what it would be like to live in your chosen destination.

Make a mask

What you need:

- books about masks
- various craft supplies

What to do:

1. Research masks, including how they are used in traditional theatre such as Japanese Noh Theatre. (Noh Theatre involves male actors or dancers wearing masks and using slow, stylised movements.)

2. Consider how colour is used in masks to show a character's emotions at a particular point in time.

3. Choose any character from literature and create a mask representing the character.

4. Explain your mask to the class and describe how your research influenced the creation of the mask.

Create a picture book

What to do:

1. Write a picture book, suitable for children aged 4–8 years, dealing with an aspect of friendship or conflict that you feel is relevant for children in this age group. Write the text and create the illustrations.

2. When you have published your book, read it to a lower primary pupil or group of pupils and ask for their opinions about your book.